Football

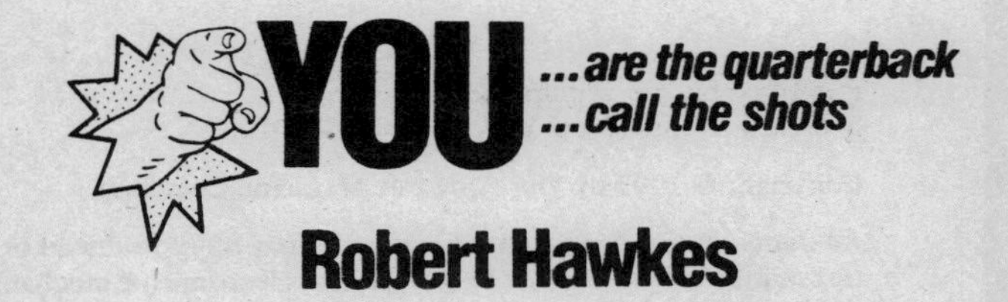

Robert Hawkes

A TRUMPET CLUB SPECIAL EDITION

Published by The Trumpet Club
666 Fifth Avenue, New York, New York 10103

ISBN 0-440-84168-2

Sports Illustrated For Kids Books is an imprint of Little, Brown and Company (Inc.)

Interior design by Aisia De'Anthony

Interior illustrations by Diana Magnuson

Printed in the United States of America
October 1992

10 9 8 7 6 5 4 3 2 1
OPM

ATTENTION!

You must read these first pages before the start of today's big game!

It has been a hot and cold season for your team, the Carolina Rebels, but now you're in the NFL playoffs! Coach Tyrone has named *you,* a rookie who earned the nickname "Rabbit" during the regular season, to be the starting quarterback. It's your chance to become a G.F.H.—a Genuine Football Hero. Opportunity is knocking. Are you up for it?

If you are, this book is for you. But you don't read it straight through like a regular book. Instead, you help create the story. *You* will be "Rabbit," the quarterback of the Carolina Rebels, and your section will be in darker, bolder type. The other voice is that of the announcer's.

This is the most important game of the season—the American Football Conference championship game—and the winner will go to the Super Bowl! The decisions you make will have a big effect on the outcome. Should you put the ball in the air, or keep it on the ground? Should you try for the first down when you face a fourth down with only inches to go, or play it safe and kick a field goal? It's all up to you. You call the plays.

Follow the directions at the end of each section to guide you to the choice you want. When you reach the end of the game, go back to the beginning and play again. This time try making some different choices. You have the possibility of 26 different outcomes for the game. How the game turns out is entirely up to you. Get ready to lead your team to Super Bowl Sunday!

OFFICIAL ROSTER

Your Team: The Carolina Rebels

Your Key Players:
***Remember:** You're the quarterback who earned the nickname "Rabbit" in training camp. Fill in your stats in the blanks. Whenever you see Rabbit mentioned in The play-by-play, that's you!*

No.	Name	Nickname
7	Caleb Castrini	"RABBIT"
23	Nelson Wicker	"NELLS"
64	Larry Brown	"BREAKER"
88	Waylon Kirby	"KILLER"
86	Mustafa Jackson	"MOE"
41	Tanner Smith	"TIGER"
9	Alonzo Vanunzo	"LOU"
85	Barry Finch	"BORIS"
19	Artie Dogan	"CLANCY"

Your Opponents: The Philadelphia Panthers

The Announcers: Jay Moore, Duke Vinson

Position	Height/Weight	College
Quarterback	5'4"/77	Penn State
Tight End	6'1"/220	Notre Dame
Center	6'1"/260	USC
Tight End	6'2"/215	Miami
Split End	5'/10"/175	Alabama
Fullback	6'3"/230	Maryland
Kicker	5'6"/160	SMU
Wide Receiver	6'2"/200	Oklahoma
Running Back	6'1"/205	Nebraska

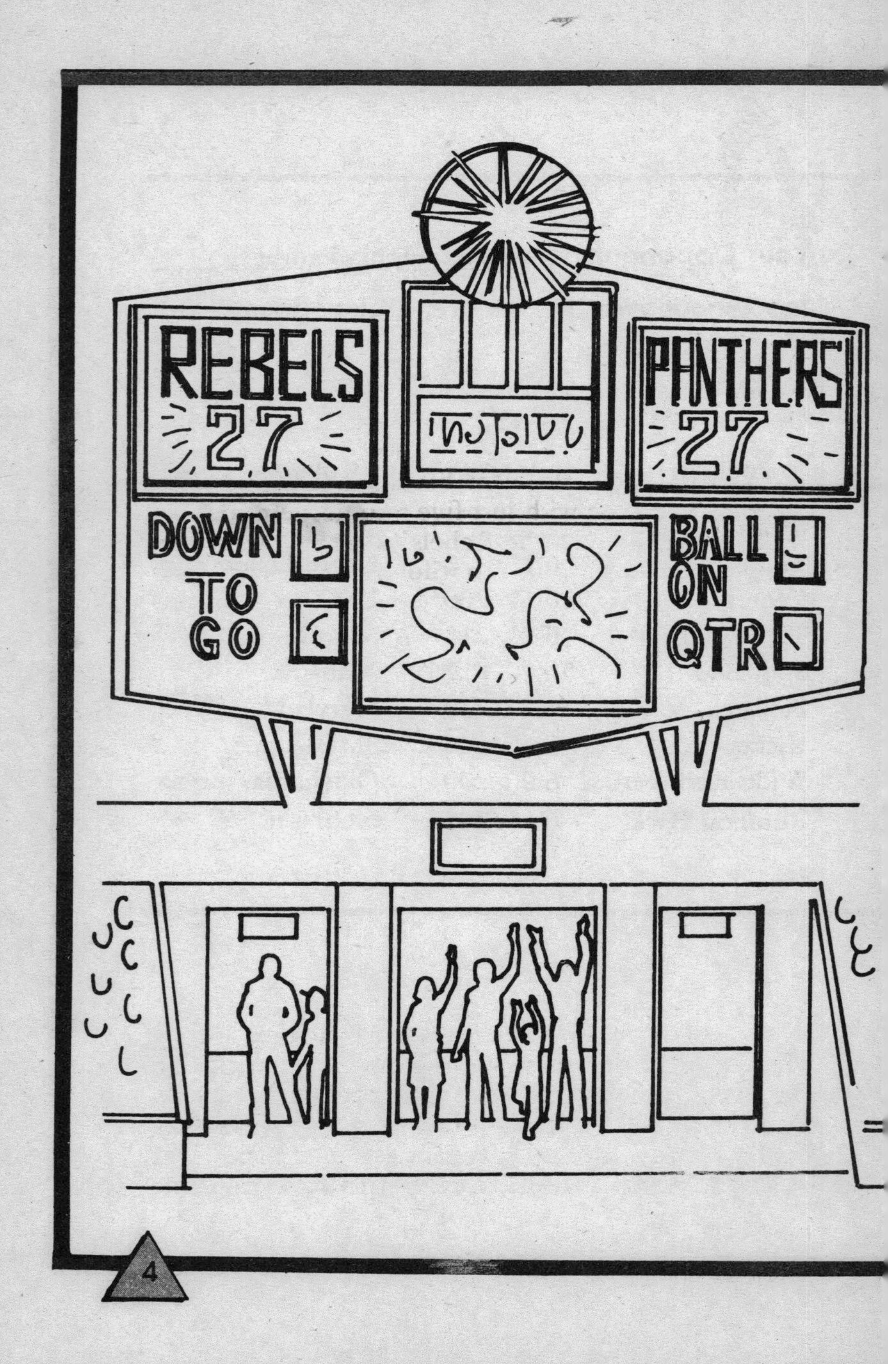
REBELS
27
PANTHERS
27
DOWN
TO GO
BALL ON
QTR

And we're back! What an incredible AFC championship game this has been so far! In case you just tuned in, I'm Jay Moore, your announcer. Alongside me here in the booth is Duke Vinson, Super Bowl veteran and former head coach of the Chicago Bisons. Are you surprised by what we've seen here today, Duke?"

"You bet, Jay. The score has gone back and forth all game, and now with just five minutes left, it's 27–27. No one expected the Rebels to do this well since they got into the playoffs as a wild-card team, while the home team Philadelphia Panthers have been to the Super Bowl twice. But the Rebs are sure giving them a run for their money. Carolina had a rough first quarter, but their defense has been holding since then, and their offense has been spectacular."

"What about Rabbit, the Rebel quarterback?"

"He had an uneven season, but he's sure played well this afternoon, Jay. He looked rattled after that last tackle, though, so we'll have to see what he can do with the ball now."

My heart is beating so hard it feels like it might jump out of my chest. In five minutes, the Rebels could go into the record books as Conference Champs! What a game this has been! Things looked terrible for us in the first quarter. Within the first five minutes the Panthers kicked a 34-yard field goal, and then kicked another three minutes later from our 27-yard line. Our defense was looking terrible. Then the Panther quarterback threw the ball right by our middle linebacker for a 20-yard touchdown pass. They made the extra point, and were beating us 13–0 at the end of the quarter.

It looked like the game was going to be a blowout. But at the start of the second quarter, we returned the kickoff to our 41-yard line. I followed up by completing a couple of short passes, calling some razzle-dazzle running plays, and then throwing a touchdown pass to my tight end, Killer Kirby. The extra point made the score 7–13. The Panthers came back with all they had after that. It looked like they would score again—until one of our cornerbacks made an amazing interception and returned it for a touchdown! The extra point was good, and suddenly we were leading, 14–13.

Our offense continued to roll during the second half, picking up 13 more points with a touchdown and two field goals. Then the Panther offense got going. They made a touchdown, trimming our lead to 27–20 at the end of the third quarter.

With just a 7-point lead, it was time for us to play very carefully. I handed off to running back, Nells Wicker, for a run up the middle—but he fumbled! The Panthers immediately came back to score another TD and that's how we got to where we are now—the score 27–27, with just five minutes left to play.

Nobody thought we would get this far, but

the whole team has been playing incredibly well. Our running backs, Nells Wicker and Clancy Dogan, have rushed for nearly 200 yards combined. A couple of short runs by our big fullback, Tiger Smith, cracked the wall of Panther defensive linemen for one of our touchdowns. And wide receiver Boris Finch has already made eight pass receptions, setting a team record for one game. Now we have a shot at going to our first Super Bowl ever. What a great way to end my rookie year!

I walk out on the field to call the next play. Our defense stopped the Panthers on their last possession and we've just received the punt. It's first down and 10 yards to go from our 34-yard line. The huddle forms. All eyes are on me. It's time to get things rolling. The Panthers have been operating mainly out of a 4-3-4 defense: They have four defensive linemen, three linebackers behind them to guard against the run, and four defensive backs prowling the backfield, ready to cover our receivers in case we throw a pass.

Our running game has been effective, so I could start off conservatively with a sweep-left—handing off to Wicker for a wide run toward the left sideline. That could gain five yards or more, and give us a lot of second-down options. But if we're aggressive, we could catch them off guard with a deep pass.

▲ *To run the sweep-left, turn to page 8.*

▲ *To pass deep, turn to page 10.*

Well, Duke, the Rebels are lined up at their 34 in a standard pro set, with running backs Nelson Wicker and Clancy Dogan behind Rabbit. Split end Moe Jackson is wide to the right. Tight end Killer Kirby lines up left, along with wide receiver Boris Finch, giving the Rebels greater strength on that side. The Panther defense is set up in a 4-3-4, ready for either a run or a pass.

There's the snap . . . and Rabbit hands the ball to Wicker, who sprints left, taking advantage of some key blocks by Kirby and Rebel fullback Tiger Smith. Wicker crosses the 35 . . . the 38 . . . the 40-yard line before he's brought down by Bobby Eldridge, the Panther cornerback, after a pickup of 7 yards. So the line of scrimmage moves to the 41, and it's second down and a short 3 yards to go.

The teams trot back up to the line. The ball is snapped. Rabbit drops deep in the pocket, looking to throw to Kirby, but Panther linebacker Phil Keller seems to have him covered. There goes the pass . . . interception!

Keller is immediately tackled by Kirby, but the Panthers take over at the Carolina 49-yard line.

Well, that was a bust. There are less than four minutes to play now. The Panthers move the ball slowly but surely toward field-goal range, but then our defense succeeds in stopping them on fourth down. So we take over at our own 31. The score's still tied at 27, but if we lose the ball this deep on our side of the field, the Panthers are sure to get a field goal before the clock runs out. We really need a first down. My first thought is that I have to pass. The only problem with that idea is that the Panthers will be expecting the pass. That could work to my advantage, though. Instead of passing I could run a reverse. In that case, I'd hand the ball off to one of my running backs, Clancy Dogan, who would start to run left. But before he crossed the line of scrimmage, he'd hand the ball off to my tight end, Killer Kirby. Then Killer would run back the other way, to the right. If the play works, the Panther defense will be running to cover the fake play on the left side of the field while Kirby scrambles right.

▲ *To run a reverse, turn to page 12.*

▲ *To throw a pass, turn to page 14.*

The Rebels take over the ball at their own 34. It's first down and 10 yards to go. They step up to the line of scrimmage in a standard pro set, with the running backs Nelson Wicker and Clancy Dogan behind Rabbit. The split end, Mustafa Jackson, is wide out to the left, and wide receiver Boris Finch is wide to the right. Waylon Kirby, the tight end, lines up close to the left, making that the strong side of the field.

The center snaps the ball to Rabbit, who drops back into the pocket formed by his offensive linemen. Rabbit fakes a pass, hesitates, then fires the ball deep. Kirby is the intended receiver, but the pass is clearly overthrown . . . and it's incomplete!

I could kick myself. I knew that pass would be too long a split second before I released it, but by then it was too late to stop. Now I have to concentrate on my options for second down, with 10 long yards to go. This is definitely a passing situation. So maybe I'll go with a screen pass to my running back, Dogan. The screen starts out like a regular pass play except that my linemen let the defensive linemen through. With everybody crashing in at me, I toss the ball over them to Dogan, who should then have blockers to lead him upfield and no

defensive linemen to contend with. The success of the play depends on my getting the ball away before the defensive players reach me.

The problem with any pass now, however, is that everybody is expecting it. If I call the screen and they blitz me—sending their linebackers or safeties after me, along with their linemen—I'm hamburger meat. So maybe I should go for a draw play instead. To do that, I'd drop back as if I were going to pass but then I'd hand the ball off to one of my running backs—probably Nells, since he's great at stretching a three-yard play into five or six.

▲ *To throw a screen pass, turn to page 16.*

▲ *To run a draw play, turn to page 18.*

This is Jay Moore, your announcer, and we're back to live action. It's first-and-10 with 3:17 left to play as the Rebel offense lines up at its 31-yard line.

The Rebels are in a standard pro set, with running backs Wicker and Dogan behind Rabbit. Tight end Killer Kirby lines up left, with split end Moe Jackson wide to the right. The Panther defense is set up in a 4-3-4 formation, looking for either a run or a pass.

Rabbit is in the shotgun formation, standing 5 or 6 yards behind the center, Larry Brown. Rabbit barks out signals while checking the defense. There's the snap! And Rabbit hands the ball to Dogan, who scampers left. But it's a reverse! Kirby takes the ball from Dogan and starts hotfooting back to the right. Kirby finds a hole and crosses the line of scrimmage, but Keller nails him at the 35-yard line.

The Panthers and the Rebels keep the same lineup at the 35 for this second down with 6 yards to go. This time Rabbit goes for the pass . . . incomplete! Now the clock reads 2:46 to go, and the Rebels face third-and-6 against this tough Panther defense. . . .

This is a tough one. We need 6 yards now, and we need them badly.

I can hear the Panther fans screaming for defense. I know they think we don't have a chance of making the first down. I'm feeling pumped now, and I'm ready to show those fans exactly how wrong they are.

The guys are waiting for me to come up with a minor miracle, and I might just have one for them—a flea-flicker. That's a trick play where I flip the ball to my wide receiver, Boris Finch. Since he is behind me, this is a lateral and not a forward pass. The defense rushes toward him, thinking he's going to run with the ball. But instead of running, Finch passes the ball long to the split end, Moe Jackson.

On the other hand, I could call a relatively safe down-and-out pass. I would simply send my receivers out and hope that at least one will be open for a pass. It's a difficult play to stop—the receiver runs right at the defender for seven or eight yards, then suddenly breaks toward the sideline. If my timing is right, the ball will be there when he makes the cut. And we'll pick up enough yards to make this critical first down.

▲ *To call the flea-flicker, turn to page 20.*

▲ *To throw the down-and-out pass, turn to page 22.*

There's 3:17 left to play, and the Rebels take over at their 31-yard line. The Panthers are in a standard 4-3-4 defense, ready for either a pass or a run. Rabbit lines up in the shotgun formation, standing about six yards behind the center so he doesn't have to drop back after the snap; this gives him a little more time to assess his players' positions before making a pass. The rest of the team is in a standard pro set, with Jackson wideout to the right and Kirby out to the left. Wide receiver Boris Finch goes into motion, trotting behind the linemen from left to right. There's the snap, and Rabbit drops back even farther, looking for first-down yardage. The Panther linebackers blitz, but Rabbit scrambles right and throws a bullet to Finch. It's complete! Finch stretches the play out to the 44 before being tackled. It's first down on the Rebels 44-yard line.

With 2:50 to play, we've got a lot riding on these next few downs. My center, Breaker Brown, thinks we should take it easy with some safe running plays and work our way into field-goal range. Once we get there we'll let Lou kick us into the Super Bowl. Killer Kirby disagrees. He's sure he can beat the Panther defense and get open for a deep pass.

They both have a point. A few solid runs could set up the field goal and put us ahead by 3 points. But that's not much of a lead. On the other hand, if I try for a long pass and the Panthers intercept it, we'll be in deep trouble.

To run, turn to page 24.

To throw a deep pass, turn to page 26.

After that incomplete pass, the Rebels are still at their own 34, and it's second-and-10 with 4:19 left to play. Rabbit is lining up in the shotgun for this play, which usually indicates a pass. He's about six yards behind the center, so he'll save the time it would take to drop back; this gives him a few seconds to see where the receivers and defenders are before letting the ball fly. The Panther defense has moved into a nickel formation: They have four down linemen at the line of scrimmage, only two linebackers and five defensive backs. With only two linebackers the Panthers are weaker against the run, but the fifth defensive back gives them better coverage of the Rebels' receivers.

There's the snap . . . and here comes the blitz! Rabbit is forced to scramble to his right. He's searching for Finch, finds him just over the line of scrimmage, and gets off a wobbly throw just as the linebackers reach him. Finch gets a hand on the ball and makes a terrific catch!

Finch picks up another 6 or 7 yards on his own, reaching the 41-yard line before being brought down. Rabbit's perfect use of the screen pass brings the Rebels to third down and 3 yards to go.

That was a success, but what should I do now? I know it's crazy, but I'm thinking about trying another short pass over the middle. After all, things went pretty well the first time, and I need only 3 yards now for the first down. Only this time I wouldn't call a screen pass. Instead, I would run a play-action fake, in which I fake a handoff to Tiger Smith, my fullback, sending him up the middle as I step back and toss a short pass to Finch again.

Still, it might make more sense to call a standard running play. If I hand off to Nells Wicker, he might be able to pick up the short yardage we need.

▲ *To call a running play, turn to page 32.*

▲ *To fake the handoff and throw another pass, turn to page 34.*

It's second down and 10 yards to go from the Rebel 34. The clock reads 4:19 as the Carolina offense moves back up to the line, obviously frustrated after having bungled that last pass.

Rabbit is in the shotgun formation, six yards behind the center. This usually—but not always—indicates a pass. This way Rabbit saves the time it would ordinarily take him to drop back, giving him a few more seconds to check out the secondary. The Panthers have gone to their nickel defense, with four down linemen at the line of scrimmage, just two linebackers and five defensive backs. This pass-prevent formation is weak against the run, but provides better coverage of the Rebel receivers.

Rabbit barks out signals. Now the ball is snapped. Instead of looking for the pass, Rabbit hands the ball to Wicker, who darts ahead. Wicker finds a hole and breaks free for an 11-yard gain and a first down at the 45. The Rebels set up for the next play with Rabbit still in the shotgun. This time he *does* go for the pass, to Kirby, who races left and is brought down beyond the Panther 46, just short of another first down.

Those last two plays went like clockwork, and now we finally have decent field position. The clock's running. If we can hold onto the

ball, I can get us into field-goal range and leave the Panthers with so little time after our kick that they probably won't be able to score. Obviously a running play is called for here—nothing spectacular, just enough to give us that yard or so for the first down. I could sneak it up the middle myself. Or maybe I should hand off to my fullback, Tiger Smith, and let him do the job. Pound for pound I'd put him up against anybody else in the league. The only problem with that option is the extra moments it takes to hand off and get Tiger forward. He could get caught behind the line, and then we'd lose a down *and* yardage.

▲ *To run a quarterback sneak, turn to page 36.*

▲ *To hand off the ball to Tiger, turn to page 38.*

The visiting Rebels are returning to the line of scrimmage now. They face a rough third-and-6 situation, with 2:46 on the clock."

"Jay, the Panther defense is still in a 4-3-4 formation, with four down linemen set up across the Rebels guards and tackles, the three Panther linebackers hedging back behind the line to guard against the run, and the four defensive backs behind them."

"I'm not sure the run is much of an option here, Duke, with less than three minutes left to play. It looks to me like they've got to go for the pass. Rabbit lines up directly behind the center, Breaker Brown, with Jackson wide to the left and Finch to the right a few steps behind the line. Tight end Kirby lines up close to the right, making that the Rebels' strong side. After a quick snap, Rabbit drops back as the offensive line forms a protective wall in front of him. Rabbit tosses the ball over to Finch. Finch looks deep downfield and rockets the ball to Jackson . . . and it's complete!

"Jackson snags the pass at midfield, shakes one defender and sprints to the Panther 43 before being brought down by two Panther defensive backs. A 22-yard gain on the play."

"A flag is down, Jay."

"That's right, Duke. One of the Panther defensive backs hit Jackson when he was already down. That's a personal foul and the officials will add another 15 yards to the Rebels' gain. It's a tough break for the Panthers. The Rebels are in excellent field-goal position with a first-and-10 at the Panther 28-yard line."

Okay, we can do this. We all feel great, but it's not over yet. The obvious move is to play it safe, *very* safe. We could get off some running plays, kill the clock, and set up the field goal. The worst thing that could happen then is Lou Vanunzo, our kicker, might blow the kick and send this game into overtime.

On the other hand, I want to be a hero as much as anybody. The one thing the Panthers *won't* be expecting is for us to go to the air. I could send all my receivers out, make a quick completion to whoever's open, and then hope he can get into the end zone.

Coach Tyrone will have my head if the ball is intercepted. I don't know if we should gamble that much, but if it works it would be beautiful to see. . . .

▲ *To pass, turn to page 44.*

▲ *To run, turn to page 46.*

The Rebels are watching the clock now. It's third down with 6 yards to go. They line up in a standard pro set at their 35-yard line. Rabbit lines up directly behind the center, Breaker Brown. The running backs are right behind Rabbit; tight end Kirby and split end Jackson are wide out to each side, with the receiver Finch also to the right. The Panthers maintain their 4-3-4 defense, with four down linemen, and the three linebackers holding back behind the line to guard against a possible run. A run doesn't seem very probable, however. The visitors have too little time and too much ground to make up.

"There's the snap, and Rabbit drops back into the pocket as all his receivers take off. The Panther blitz is on, with the three Panther linebackers charging at Rabbit. Rabbit sprints right. He scrambles, searching for a receiver, and is forced to pass early. It's a long ball intended for Jackson. He jumps for it. He has the ball in his hands . . . but he bobbles it and it falls incomplete. The Carolina fans are not happy with that one at all, Duke."

"I like the audacity of a play like that, Jay. Rabbit obviously has guts, but sometimes guts aren't enough. The Rebels are facing a punting situation now, with a fourth-and-6 from their own 35 and the clock stopped by the incompletion at 2:40."

Fourth down. I can feel the sense of doom that has settled over the huddle. I have to shake the guys out of it with the next play. If we punt, and the Panthers make a mistake deep in their own territory, we could regain possession and be in great scoring position. Even if they don't blow it, our defense might be able to keep them from scoring and get us the ball back or send this game into overtime.

Our other option would be to *fake* the punt, go for broke, and try to pick up the first down with a short pass. The only problem is that if the play bombs, we'll be turning the ball over to the Panthers on our side of the field. They wouldn't need to move the ball very far to get into field-goal position. It's life or death now. Either way we go it's a gamble. . . .

▲ *To punt, turn to page 47.*

▲ *To fake the punt, turn to page 48.*

There's 2:40 on the clock as Rabbit's offense moves back up to the 44-yard line. They go into a standard pro set, with running backs Wicker and Dogan behind Rabbit, split end Jackson wide to the right, and wide receiver Finch wide to the left. The tight end, Kirby, lines up left, too, making that the Rebels' strong side. The Panthers are in a standard 4-3-4 defense, looking for either a run or a pass.

Rabbit calls the signals. There's the snap to Rabbit, who hands the ball to Clancy Dogan. Dogan charges right, getting some extra blocking from Jackson and Tiger Smith, the fullback, who leads the play just outside the right tackle. Dogan is finally brought down on the Panther 49 after a pickup of seven yards. And so the Rebs face second down and 3 yards to go. The clock is running, with 2:24 remaining.

That worked out pretty well, but time is running out now and everybody knows it. We're all breathing hard and slapping our hands on our knee pads as we scramble back to the huddle. Our next play is critical.

The Panthers must be looking for another run, or even a series of runs. And why not? Running plays control the ball in two ways: 1) they help us get into field-goal range and 2)

they help kill the clock, so that even if we don't win it with the field goal, we'll force the game into overtime.

But why do what they expect? Instead, I could run a play-action fake. In that case I pretend to hand off to Dogan. If we're lucky, the Panther linebackers will wait behind the line of scrimmage a few extra seconds until they realize that Dogan doesn't really have the ball. And that's all the time I'll need to make a pass to Finch and put this game away right now.

▲ *To call another running play, turn to page 28.*

▲ *To call a play-action fake, turn to page 30.*

There's 2:41 left to play, and the Rebels have a first-and-10 at their 44-yard line. Rabbit stands back in the shotgun again, five or six yards behind center. Finch and Kirby are wide out to the right, Jackson to the left. The Panthers have assumed their nickel defense; they have four down linemen at the line of scrimmage, just two linebackers, and five defensive backs instead of the usual four. This is a pass-prevent formation.

"The ball is snapped to Rabbit. He's checking out his options. And there goes the pass. Rabbit's throwing deep. Killer Kirby stretches . . . it's complete, which brings it to the Panther 39! Rabbit's passing game is really starting to click, Duke."

"You said it, Jay. They've managed two first downs in a row and are driving into an excellent position to score and break this tie."

All right! This is fun. I have to keep this drive alive. The guys are ready for me to call the next play. A pass would be too obvious, so I'm definitely going with a running play this down. The only question is, what kind of running play? I could run a trap play. That means our right guard blocks the Panther linebacker facing our center, our right tackle blocks their inside down lineman and our tight end blocks

their outside linebacker. Since their defensive end remains open, he'll charge in, and our left guard will move over to pick him up behind the line of scrimmage. If things are working properly, a nice big hole should open up between the right guard and the tackle, and Wicker can plow right through it. Nells is perfect for this play; he's so fast on his feet it's amazing he doesn't lose his shoes half the time.

Another possibility would be to go with a reverse. That means I hand off to my running back. He starts to go left but then hands off to my tight end before crossing the line of scrimmage. The tight end then takes off right, while the Panther defense scrambles left to cover our running back. I like tricky plays like that, and it would have a good chance to work here.

▲ *To run a trap play, turn to page 40.*

▲ *To run a reverse, turn to page 42.*

The Rebels line up at the Panther 49 in the same standard pro set. Rabbit checks out the defense as he calls the signals. There's the snap. Rabbit hands the ball to Dogan again. *Fumble!* The exchange wasn't made! The ball is loose behind the line of scrimmage. The Panthers recover on the 50-yard line with less than two minutes left to play!

The Panthers aren't losing any time. They march downfield with a series of short passes and score a touchdown with just 26 seconds left on the clock. After making the extra point, they kick off to the Rebels. Carolina has time to get off only two desperation bomb passes before the buzzer sounds. The Panthers clinch a Super Bowl berth, winning by 7.

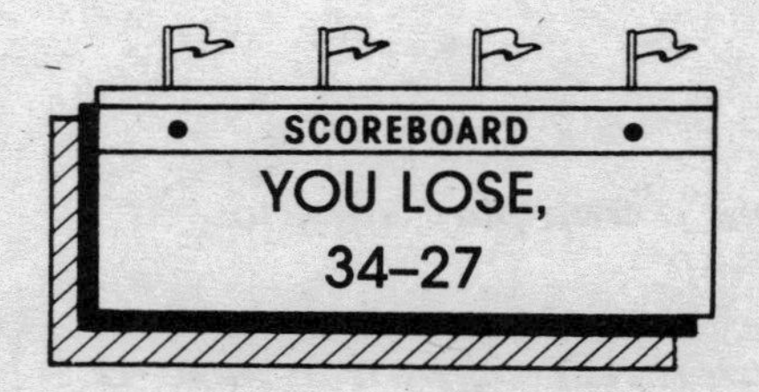

19

The Rebs rush back up to the line. They go into the same setup as before, with Wicker and Dogan behind Rabbit, Jackson wide to the right, and Kirby and Finch to the left. The Panthers go into their 4-3-4.

There's the snap. Rabbit hands off to Dogan, who plows right as before, getting the same extra blocking. But no—it's a fake handoff and Rabbit still has the ball. He's dropping back, looking for a receiver downfield and—yes!—he lets it go deep.

It's a footrace for the ball between Panther defensive back Cecil Andreas and Rebel tight end Killer Kirby. The ball is up for grabs, and . . . it's *intercepted!* Andreas has it at the Panther 18, and he's heading back into Rebel territory. He's at the 50, the 40, the 30! He's going to go all the way with it. *Touchdown!*

The extra point is up . . . and it's wide, so the score is now 33–27 with just 1:46 left to play.

It's going to take a miracle to pull us out of this one. We need a touchdown—and fast. The kickoff return team gets us decent field position at the 36. The coach points a finger at me and asks if I can handle the situation and I tell him, "Absolutely." I can feel that all eyes are on me. With only 1:40 on the clock, we have to go to the air. The choice is simple. We can either send everybody out—I call it "desperation city," but the playbook would call it a deep pass—or we can run a series of quick, short patterns and hope we get down the field fast enough. Either way, an interception kills us.

▲ *To throw a deep pass, turn to page 74.*

▲ *To throw a series of short passes, turn to page 76.*

It's third down and 3 yards to go as the Rebels move back up to their 41-yard line. They line up in a standard pro set, with running backs Nells Wicker and Clancy Dogan behind Rabbit, split end Moe Jackson and tight end Killer Kirby out to the left, and wide receiver Boris Finch out to the right. The Panther defense is aligned in a standard 4-3-4, ready for either a run or a pass.

"Rabbit calls the signals . . . and there's the snap. Rabbit hands the ball to Wicker, the halfback. Wicker powers his way up the middle . . . but he's nailed at the line of scrimmage for no gain. The Panthers were certainly ready for that run, Duke."

"The Rebels have to make a very tough decision now, Jay. It's fourth and a short 3, but they're looking at it from the wrong side of the field."

What a bust! The clock shows a little more than three minutes left.

There are two ways for me to go. If we follow the game plan and punt, there's a good chance that our defense will be able to keep them from scoring so we can get the ball back or send the game into overtime.

On the other hand, I could go with a short pass for the first down. There's a chance it

won't work and the Panthers would take possession on our side of the field. But if the play succeeds, we'll all be so pumped nothing will be able to stop us.

▲ *To pass, turn to page 49.*

▲ *To punt, turn to page 50.*

It's third down and 3 to go from the Rebel 41, with 3:41 left to play. The Rebs go into a standard pro set, this time with Wicker and fullback Tiger Smith behind Rabbit, wide receiver Finch out right, and tight end Kirby and split end Jackson lining up left. The Panthers go into a standard 4-3-4 formation. They're ready for either the run or another pass.

Jackson goes in motion to the right as Rabbit calls the signals. There's the snap. Rabbit hands off to Smith . . . But no, it's a *fake* handoff, and Rabbit still has the ball. He drops back, looking for a receiver. The linebackers are coming at him now, but Finch curls around behind them and Rabbit just barely gets a pass off to him. Finch grabs the ball and is off again, bolting forward! He makes another great run, advancing to the Panther 48 before being brought down. Eleven yards on the play. It's first down and a new lease on life for the Rebels!

Okay, we're in Panther territory with a little more than three minutes to go. As I head back to the huddle I tell the guys it's time to play hard and fast, and they let out a cheer. It's decision time. We're at the Panther 48. All we need to do is work our way into field-goal territory. My first inclination is to throw a series of rapid short passes and just move the ball forward.

On the other hand, maybe we can catch them off guard with some razzle-dazzle. The double reverse might be just the thing. I would set up the play as if it's a sweep, handing off to my running back, Clancy Dogan. But instead of rounding the corner and running upfield, he'd hand the ball off to Boris Finch, who would rush the other way. The real trick, though, is that Finch would hand off *again,* this time to the split end, Moe Jackson, who would take off in the original direction. If it works, this crazy play might confuse the defense enough for Moe to pick up a terrific gain. And if any of the runners gets caught behind the line of scrimmage, we'll still have three more downs to make up the extra yardage.

▲ *To throw a series of short passes, turn to page 53.*

▲ *To run the double reverse, turn to page 54.*

There's 3:24 left to play as the Rebel offense returns to the line of scrimmage. It's second and inches to go, with the Rebels bearing down on the Panther 45-yard line. This is obviously a running situation, and the visitors line up accordingly in a one-back offense: Fullback Tiger Smith is behind Rabbit, and a second tight end is brought in, creating a balanced line, so that Tiger can run behind good blocking on either side. The Panther defense lines up in a 3-4-4, short-yardage, run-prevent formation. They have three down linemen, four linebackers to tackle running backs and four defensive backs to cover the receivers.

Rabbit shouts out a quick count. There's the snap. Rabbit hands off . . . no, he *fakes* to Smith and plows ahead himself. It's a quarterback sneak! Diving over the center, Rabbit has a first down! The visitors are now operating from the Panther 45, steadily advancing down the field.

Good play! The guys are yelling, slapping me on the back, and it feels great. It's time to call the next one, and I can do just about anything I want. That's the beauty of a first down on the other team's side of the field. I want to go with a pass, but which one? I could run a play-action fake, pretending to hand off to a

running back and forcing the Panther line-backers to hesitate a few moments until they see that I still have the ball. This would give me valuable time to complete a short, over-the-middle pass. We'd only pick up 5 yards or so—unless the receiver finds a hole somewhere—but it's a fairly high-percentage pass.

The other alternative would be to simply drop back into the pocket and send my receivers out on a medium cut—meaning that they would run about 15 or 16 yards and then cut in or out for the pass. A catch would give us another first down and put us into field-goal range. That's not a bad situation to be in as the clock ticks down.

▲ *To run a play-action fake, turn to page 56.*

▲ *To drop back and throw a medium-range pass, turn to page 57.*

The Rebels return to the line of scrimmage with just 3:24 left to play. It's second-and-inches, and the visitors are in good field position just past the Panther 46. It's a running situation. The Rebels are bringing in two tight ends, going with a one-back formation. The two tight ends provide strong blocking on both sides of the field so that the lone running back can run either left or right. The Panthers are set up in their 3-4-4 defense—only three down linemen, four linebackers to stop the run and four defensive backs ready to cover the pass.

"Breaker Brown snaps the ball. Rabbit hands it to Tiger Smith, the fullback. Smith drives up the middle . . . but he's nailed behind the line of scrimmage for a loss of about half a yard. Now it's third-and-1, Duke."

"Ouch. They didn't go anywhere with that play, Jay. The Rebels better hope Rabbit's got something more effective up his sleeve for this critical third down."

Uh-oh. That took a little of the wind out of our sails. Everybody seems a little down. Every decision counts now. Tiger thinks I should hand off to him again and go for another run. He might be right, but the Panther defense is pumped up now, and if they stop him again, we'll be too far away to make the field goal on fourth down.

Another option would be to run the bootleg. That means I fake the handoff to Tiger, then hide the ball as I run left and give it to my running back, Nells Wicker, who would follow Tiger's block and maybe get the first down.

▲ *To try another run, turn to page 58.*

▲ *To run the bootleg, turn to page 60.*

We're back again to live action, and it's first-and-10 for the Rebels from the Panther 39. There's 2:20 on the clock as the offense moves back up to the line of scrimmage in a standard pro set, with running backs Wicker and Dogan behind Rabbit. Tight end Killer Kirby lines up left, along with wide receiver Boris Finch; that's the Rebels' strong side. Split end Moe Jackson is wide to the right. The Panther defense is set up in a 4-3-4 alignment, alert for a possible run.

"There's the snap, and Rabbit hands the ball to Wicker, who takes off right. But instead of sweeping right he breaks through the hole between the guard and tackle, picking up some serious yardage with the trap play before he's nailed at the Panther 21-yard line.

"The clock is still running. The Rebels skip the huddle and Rabbit calls a play at the line of scrimmage. After the snap he drops back . . . he's looking long . . . Kirby is open just short of the end zone. Rabbit sees him. He throws. It's complete, and Kirby scoots in for the touchdown!"

"That was brilliantly executed, Jay. Now Lou Vanunzo goes in for the extra point. The kick is up and it's good."

The Panthers take possession with less than two minutes left, but the Rebel defense holds on and the clock runs out before they can score. The Carolina Rebels win, 34–27, and are on their way to their first-ever Super Bowl!

After that beautifully executed pass, it's first-and-10 on the Panther 39-yard line. The Rebel offense approaches the line of scrimmage in a standard pro set, with running backs Wicker and Dogan behind Rabbit. Kirby lines up left this time, along with split end Moe Jackson, while Finch is wide to the right. The Panther defense is set up in a standard 4-3-4, ready for either a run or another pass. There's 2:20 left to play.

Rabbit barks out the signals. There's the snap, and he hands the ball to Dogan, who sprints left. But then Dogan gives the ball to Kirby, who races back to the right. It's a reverse. Kirby hesitates, then finds some running room and crosses the line of scrimmage for a gain of 5 yards before he's brought down at the 34-yard line.

It's second down and 5 yards to go. The clock's running with less than two minutes left. It's time for me to break the tie and win this thing. Maybe it's time for the "Hail Mary" pass. I'll send all my receivers deep into the end zone and throw the ball up, praying that one of our guys catches it for the score.

On the other hand, it would probably be safer to call a straight running play. That would allow us to pound the ball in closer for

the field goal. We can wind down the clock at the same time, so that the Panthers won't have enough time to come back to score a field goal or touchdown of their own. Should I gamble or play it safe?

▲ *To throw a "Hail Mary" pass, turn to page 78.*

▲ *To call a running play, turn to page 81.*

This is a golden opportunity for the visitors, Duke. It's first-and-10 from the Panther 28-yard line, with 2:28 left to play. They've got plenty of time to put this thing away."

"Jay, the Panther defense has assumed a standard 4-3-4 alignment."

"The Rebels go into a standard pro set. Rabbit lines up directly behind center, with Jackson and Finch wide out to each side, and Kirby close on the left. There's the snap . . . and Rabbit fades back into his pocket. The offensive line is crumbling. The Panther defense is all over him. Rabbit is forced to scramble left. He throws the ball deep to the tight end and . . . *yes!* Kirby has it on the 5, and he scoots in for a touchdown!"

"What a great play, Jay. Killer Kirby is one of those guys who always seem to come up with something extra when the Rebels need it most. The touchdown makes the score 33–27, as Lou Vanunzo goes in to attempt the extra point."

That's the way the whole game should go! Except—oh no! Lou blew the extra point, kicking the ball wide to the left. Too late to worry now. This is a tricky situation, because there are still over two minutes on the clock—enough time for the Panthers to score.

I think we might try for an onsides kick. That means we kick the ball short—though it has to go at least 10 yards—and hope the bouncing ball touches one of the Panther players. Then we can try to fall on it to regain possession before the Panthers get control of it.

The onsides kick has a high failure rate, but the receiving team probably won't be expecting it, which gives us a slight edge. Besides, we need to get the ball back *now.*

If I don't go for an onsides kick, we could kick the ball deep and let our defense try to hold the Panthers. That's what they're paid for, and I know they're up for it.

▲ *To call an onsides kick, turn to page 63.*

▲ *To kick deep, turn to page 64.*

The visiting Rebels are really on a hot streak now. It's first-and-10 from the Panther 28-yard line. There's 2:28 left to play, plenty of time for Carolina to score and put this thing away.

The Panthers have gone to a standard 4-3-4 defense. Rabbit calls his signals and there's the snap. Rabbit makes a quick handoff to Clancy Dogan. Wait . . . there's a problem. Fumble! The ball popped loose on the exchange, and there's a pack of Panthers all over Dogan, fighting for the ball. The Panthers recover it! That's a critical turnover, Duke.

The Panther offense has taken complete control at this point. Its merciless passing attack picks apart the Rebel defense and finishes the drive with a 14-yard touchdown pass. The extra point is good, and the score is now 34–27, Panthers. With less than a minute of play left, the Rebels receive the kickoff, but the clock runs out before Rabbit can move the ball past the Rebels' own 30.

The Panthers win the AFC championship!

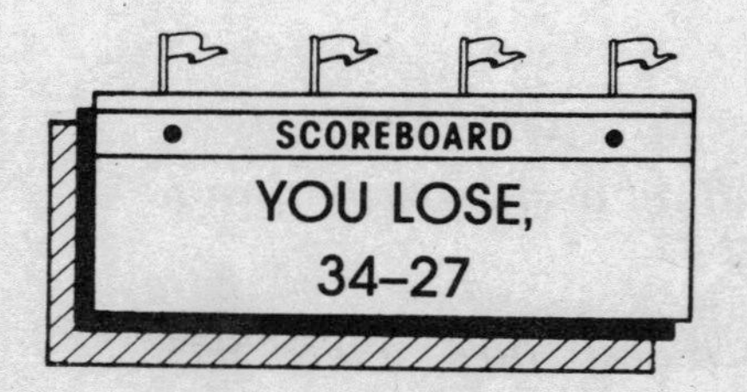

The Rebels punting team takes the field at the visitors' 35. It's fourth down and a long 6 yards to go with 2:40 left to play. The Rebel kicker, Lou Vanunzo, will make the punt. There's the snap. The Panthers rush Vanunzo—they're going to try to block the kick rather than set up a good punt return. It looks like the kick is away . . . but no, it's blocked! There's a terrific scramble as the ball flies loose. The Panthers' Wes Louis grabs it. He breaks free and crosses the 20, the 10 . . . Louis is in for the touchdown! He spikes the ball in the end zone while the fans are on their feet screaming. The Panthers miss the extra point, but they still lead the Rebels 33–27.

The Rebels receive the kickoff, but Rabbit's offense just can't come back after that blocked punt. The clock winds down, and the Panthers win the AFC championship and a trip to the Super Bowl.

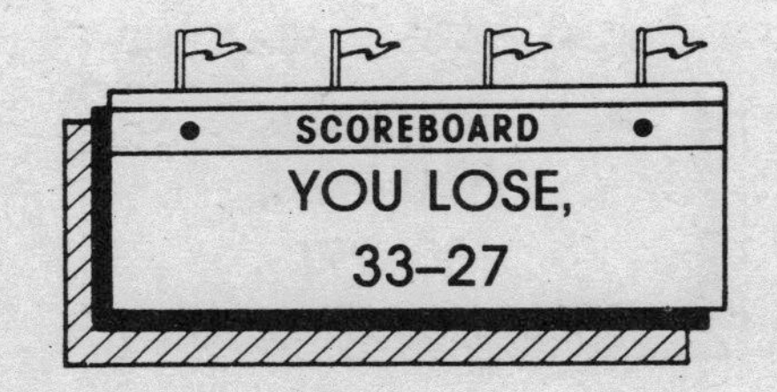

The Rebels punting unit lines up at the Rebel 35-yard line. It's fourth-and-6 with 2:40 on the clock.

"There's the snap, and the Panthers rush to block the ball. But wait . . . it's a fake punt! Lou Vanunzo, the Rebel kicker, has the ball and he's rolling right. He lobs a short pass to Moe Jackson, and Jackson picks up the first down and more, going all the way to the Panther 47 before he's brought down."

"That play was a big gamble, Jay, but it sure paid off. The Rebels are now in really good shape for the final two minutes."

After three perfectly executed running plays, the Rebs try for the field goal—and it's good! Now the Panthers receive the kickoff with just over 30 seconds on the clock. But after the thrashing they received from the Rebels "pull-out-the-stops" offense, they don't get very far. The Rebels win the game to become this year's AFC champs. They're on their way to the Super Bowl!

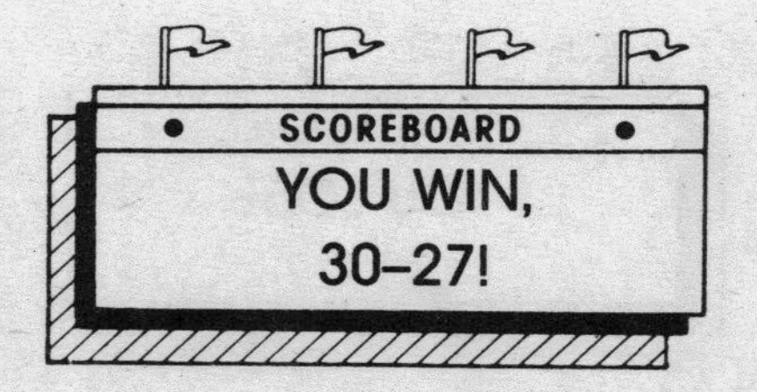

The clock reads 3:19, and it's fourth down and 3 to go from the Carolina 41-yard line. The Rebels go into a standard pro set, but the tight end comes in close to the right this time, making that their strong side. The Panthers have gone to their standard 4-3-4 defense.

"There goes the snap. The pass rush is on, but Rabbit looks right and gets off an effortless pass to Finch, who's right at the line of scrimmage. Finch reaches for the ball, grabs it, and bolts forward. He's up to the 45, crosses the midfield mark, and keeps on going! Oh—he's brought down on the Panther 38. What a terrific run, Duke!"

"Yes, indeed, Jay, 21 yards in all. That might have been the turning point of the game."

"The Rebels work their way down to the 7-yard line before being forced by the Panther defense to try for a field goal—which is good! With a little more than a minute on the clock, the Panthers receive the kickoff. But they can't get the ball into Rebels territory. The clock winds down and the buzzer sounds with the Rebels 3 points ahead. Carolina wins the AFC championship—and it's on to the Super Bowl!"

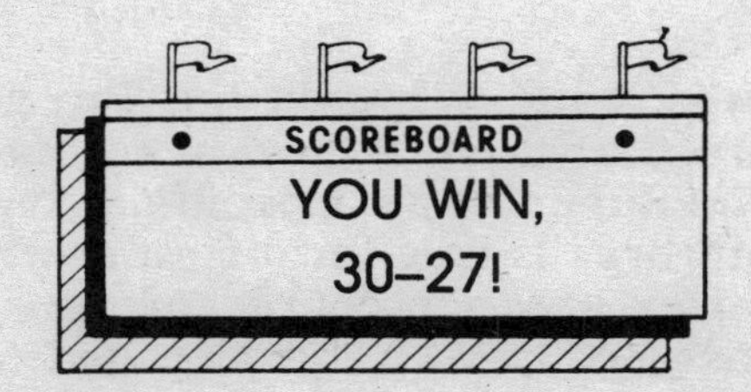

It's fourth down now, and the Rebels still have to pick up 3 yards from their 41 for the first down. There's 3:19 left to play as the Carolina punting team takes the field. Lou Vanunzo will make the kick. What do you think, Duke? Do the Panthers wait for it, or attempt a block?"

"They're going for the block, I think, Jay. Even if the worst happens and they draw a penalty for roughing the kicker, the Rebels will still be stuck on their own side of the field. And if they get the block, they're in perfect shape for a quick touchdown—or at least a field goal."

"There's the snap. The Panthers come with an all-out rush, but Vanunzo gets the kick away! Ferris, the Panther receiver, is under the ball at the Panther 19 . . . but it bounces off his hands! The ball is loose at the 22 and both sides are scrambling for it. The Rebels have it! Rabbit's going to get another chance, this time from the Panther 28."

That was a lucky break, but I'm going to need more than luck if I want to take these guys to the Super Bowl. I decide to try a run, and Dogan breaks free for a first down at the 18. But after another couple of runs and a screen pass, we have only managed to move

forward 6 yards. Now it's fourth down and 4 yards to go from the Panther 12-yard line. Only 47 seconds are left on the clock, and I'm facing a tough decision. This could be our last play in regulation time. If we score we win; if we are still tied, we go into overtime.

The safe thing to do would be to let Lou Vanunzo try to kick the field goal for three points. But even if we make it, the Panthers would have time left to try a desperation pass for a touchdown to beat us. Our other choice is to run a pass play and go for the touchdown ourselves. Even if we don't get the TD, we might pick up the first down, and that would allow us to keep possession until we go into OT. A trip to the Super Bowl's on the line here. Do we gamble or play it safe?

▲ *To attempt the field goal, turn to page 61.*

▲ *To try for the touchdown, turn to page 62.*

With 3:18 left to play, the Rebels offense lines up at the Panther 48-yard line. The Rebels are in a standard pro set, with Jackson wide out to the left and Kirby wide to the right. Finch lines up right too, making that the Rebels' strong side. The defense is back in their 4-3-4 setup.

There's the snap. Rabbit uses the pocket well, taking his time before throwing a short pass to Jackson for a gain of 7 yards. Rabbit skips the huddle and calls an audible at the line of scrimmage. The ball is snapped, and again Rabbit goes to the air, over the top to Killer Kirby for another completion and the first down. This is turning out to be a brilliant series of quick, short passes. They keep plugging down the field, and six plays later Rabbit connects with Finch for a nine-yard touchdown pass! The extra point is good, too.

The Panthers receive the kick with 30 seconds left, but it's not enough. The Rebels win the AFC championship, 34–27!

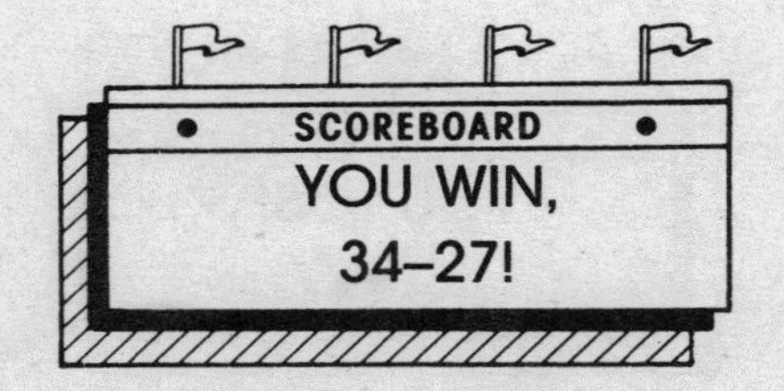

The Rebels look fired up as they break the huddle. It's first-and-10 at the Panther 48-yard line, and the clock reads 3:18. The Rebs go into a standard pro set, with running backs Wicker and Dogan behind Rabbit, tight end Killer Kirby lining up left, and split end Moe Jackson wide to the right. The Panthers set up in a 4-3-4 defense.

Rabbit shouts out the signals. The center snaps the ball, and Rabbit hands it off to Dogan, who moves quickly left. But it's a reverse, and Kirby takes the ball from Dogan and starts to run back to the right. Now Kirby hands it off again, to Finch!

It's a razzle-dazzle play, all right, a double reverse. But the Panther linebackers aren't fooled. The rush is on, and . . . *bam!* Finch is nailed behind the line of scrimmage for a loss of 4 yards.

The Panthers continue to hold Carolina on their next two plays. Then a fourth-down pass intended for Kirby is intercepted. The Panthers begin an intense two-minute drive, which ends in a perfect kick for a field goal from the Rebels 32-yard line as the clock runs out. The Panthers win the AFC championship, 30–27, and go on to the Super Bowl.

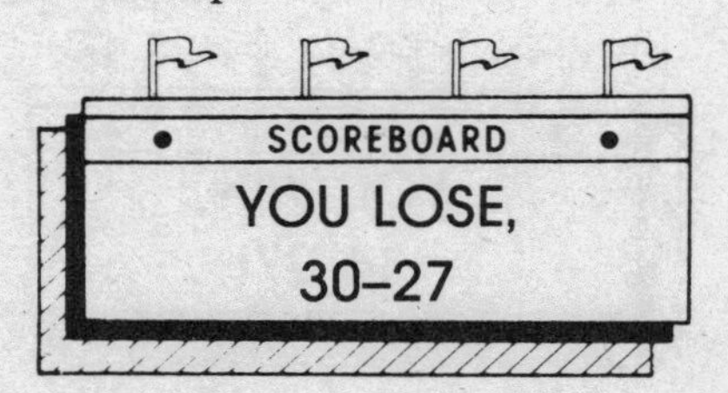

78
38

After a short huddle, the Rebels return to the line of scrimmage. They have good field position on the Panther 45. It's first down, with a little less than three minutes of play left. The Panthers assume a standard 4-3-4 defense. The Rebels go into a standard pro set, with Jackson wide out to the right and Finch and Kirby out to the left.

Brown snaps the ball to Rabbit, who starts back before handing off to Clancy Dogan. No . . . it's a play-action fake. Rabbit still has the ball, and he's looking deep. Kirby and Jackson are both open, and Rabbit lets go of the pass just before getting slammed from behind by a Panther lineman. The spiral heads straight for Kirby, and he's got it at the 19! He could go all the way . . . *yes!* A masterpiece pass from Rabbit to Kirby. And Lou Vanunzo's extra point is good! The Rebels lead, 34–27. The Panthers receive the kick with two minutes to go. They move close enough to kick a field goal. But that won't win it for them, so they go for the touchdown and are stopped cold. As time runs out, Rabbit is named the game's Most Valuable Player and the Rebels are on their way to the Super Bowl!

The offense seems determined to score in these final three minutes. It's first-and-10 as the Rebels line up on the Panther 45 in a standard pro set. Rabbit is directly behind the center, with Jackson wide out to the left and Kirby wide out to the right. Finch is also to the right, making that the Rebels' strong side. The Panther defense is back in a 4-3-4 lineup now.

"There's the snap. Rabbit falls back and is looking to pass. But the blitz is on and Rabbit gets sacked seven yards behind the line of scrimmage. Now the Rebels line up at their own 48-yard line. Just as the center snaps the ball again, an official throws a penalty flag. It's an offsides call against the Rebels! One of their guards jumped before the snap."

"It doesn't look good for the visitors, Jay. The Rebs now face second down with 22 yards to go."

Rabbit is sacked again on the second down, and two downs later the Rebels are forced to punt. The Panthers get the ball in good field position and quickly maneuver into field-goal range. The 39-yard attempt is good! As time runs out, the Panthers win, 30–27. The Panthers will make their third Super Bowl appearance in five years.

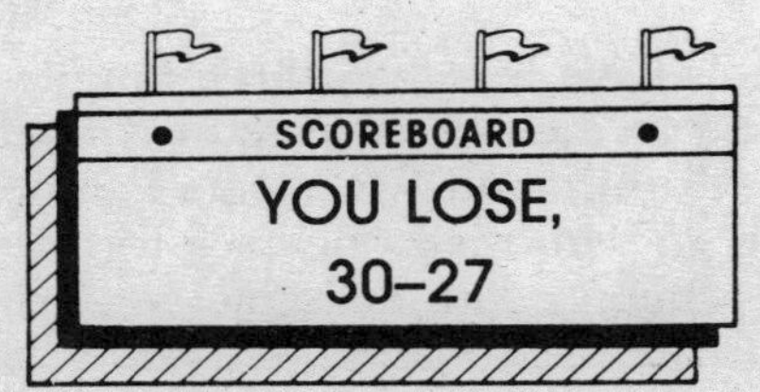

The Rebels have less than three minutes to break this 27–27 tie as their offense returns to the line of scrimmage. It's third-and-1 from the Panther 46. The Rebels again go with their one-back formation, while the Panthers counter with the same 3-4-4 run-prevent lineup.

"Rabbit barks out a quick count. There's the snap, and the handoff again goes to Tiger Smith, the fullback. Smith fights his way up the middle . . . and breaks through for 5 yards before being tackled. First down! Rabbit showed a lot of guts going to Smith again after that last stop."

"Absolutely, Jay, absolutely."

Tiger and I are both grinning. I don't want to push our luck, though. I decide to go next with a couple of conservative runs and short passes. Bit by bit we work our way deeper into Panther territory, until with just 58 seconds to play, we find ourselves in a fourth-and-1 situation on the Panther 7-yard line.

Now I have to decide whether to take a chance on the field goal—if we miss, the Panthers will get the ball back with a little bit of time left to win the game. Or I could try a quick run to pick up the first down. It's decision time.

▲ *To kick the field goal, turn to page 87.*

▲ *To run for the first down, turn to page 88.*

The Rebel offense returns to the line of scrimmage after getting crunched on that last running play. It's third down and 1 yard to go from the Panther 46-yard line, with about three minutes left to play.

The Rebels go into a standard pro set, with running backs Wicker and Smith behind Rabbit. Kirby is out to the right on this one. The Panther defense is set up in a 3-4-4 run-prevent lineup, with an extra linebacker to plug up the middle.

Rabbit calls the signals. The center snaps the ball. Rabbit hands off to Tiger Smith, who barrels toward the middle . . . but no, it's a bootleg! Rabbit still has the ball. Then he rolls left and hands it off to Wicker. But Wicker trips! He's down behind the line of scrimmage. That makes it fourth down and at least a yard and a half to go.

That failed play forces the Rebels to punt, and the Panthers start their own long drive. As the final seconds of the game tick down, their kicker makes a 21-yard field goal. The Panthers win the AFC championship, 30–27, and are Super Bowl bound!

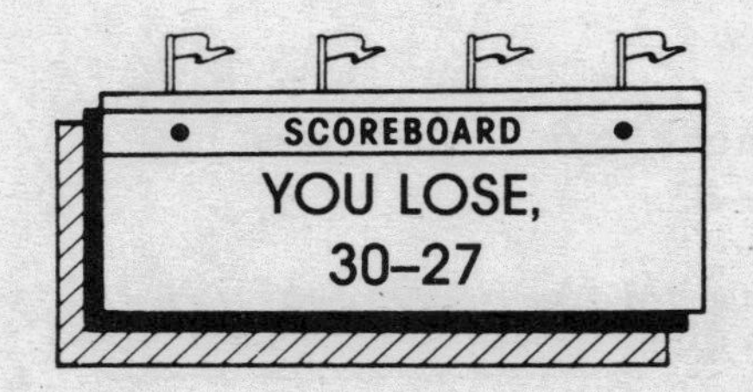

The Rebels are facing a fourth-and-4 situation from the Panther 12. There are just 47 seconds left on the clock as the Carolina kicking team takes the field. There's the snap, and the ball is placed for Vanunzo's kick. A terrific Panther rush is on, but Vanunzo gets the ball in the air. It's long enough . . . it's straight enough . . . it's good! With 33 seconds left to play, the Carolina Rebels take a 3-point lead.

The Panthers get the ball back after the kickoff, but there just isn't enough time. Their kicker attempts a desperate 52-yard last-second field goal, but it's off to the right. And so the Carolina Rebels win the AFC championship, 30–27, and are Super Bowl bound!

Only 47 seconds remain in the game as the Rebels line up for this critical fourth-down play from the Panther 12. This is a surprise, Duke. The Panthers have played some amazing defense, but the Rebels will go for the touchdown rather than settle for three points. Rabbit lines up in the shotgun with four receivers spread out to the left and right. The Panthers counter with a pass-prevent nickel defense, using four defensive backs to cover the receivers.

The center snaps the ball to Rabbit. But the Panthers are putting on a big rush. Rabbit is forced to pass early, and he barely gets the throw away. It's intended for Jackson . . . but it's intercepted!

The Panther defensive back dodges around a pack of Rebels. Now he races back the other way. The Rebels can't get anywhere near him! He makes a dazzling 85-yard run for the touchdown! The extra point is not good, but the Panthers jump ahead, 33–27.

That's a tough break for the Rebels, Duke. They'll get the ball back with just 19 seconds on the clock. They make two desperate attempts to pass deep but they're incomplete. The Panthers win it by 6, sending the Carolina Rebels home to watch the Super Bowl on TV.

SCOREBOARD

YOU LOSE,
33–27

There's 2:05 left to play as the visiting Carolina Rebels line up to kick. They lead by 6 points, 33–27, as we wind down to the final two minutes of this game. Hey, Duke, do you see what *I* see?"

"I sure do. The Rebels are lining up for an onsides kick. They are obviously attempting to deny the home team possession, but if they don't succeed, the Panthers could take over near the midfield mark—or worse—their own territory."

"That's either the gutsiest move I've seen all season or it's the stupidest, Duke. It's a *very* low percentage play. The whistle blows . . . there's Vanunzo's kick . . . and it's quickly covered by Panther Lyndon Carver at the Rebel 48. That turned out to be a very bad decision."

Taking advantage of the remaining time, the Panthers advance the ball with running plays, moving steadily deeper into Rebel territory. Then on the seventh play of the drive, the Panthers score with a 14-yard touchdown pass! The score is tied now, 33–33, as the Panther kicker goes for the extra point . . . and it's good! The Panthers win a squeaker in the final seconds, 34–33.

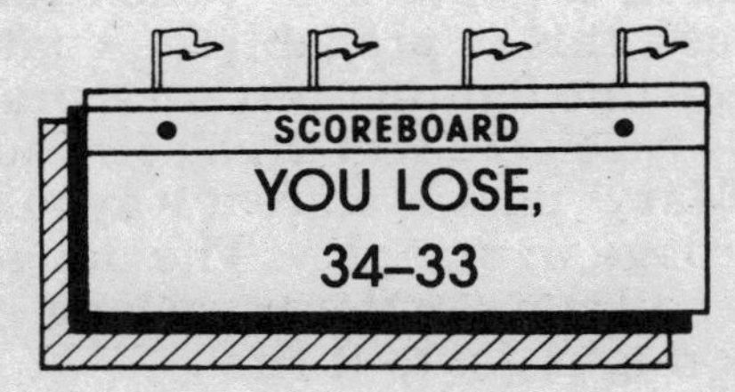

With 2:05 left to play, the visitors line up to kick. The Rebels lead by 6, 33–27, as we enter the final two minutes of this football game. Lou Vanunzo gets off a good kick, and the Panthers bring the ball back out to their 33-yard line.

But the Carolina defense begins to falter, and in less than a minute's playing time, the Panthers score a touchdown and the extra point to suddenly take the lead, 34–33. Oh, my!

After all that sweat and hard work, we're going into the final 58 seconds *one point behind.* We've got less than a minute to get back into field-goal range and pull this one out of the fire.

Our special-teams guys don't move the ball very far and we take over at our 22-yard line. There are only about 45 seconds left now. If any point in a game ever called for a "Hail Mary" pass, this is probably it. That means I throw deep into Panther territory, praying that one of my receivers will break free to catch it. A "Hail Mary" pass is a great way to pick up a lot of yardage in one play. The danger is that since the ball stays in the air so long, one of the Panthers might get to it first.

It might be a better idea to catch the defense by surprise and pitch the ball wide to my running back, Clancy Dogan. If we play it right, he could fly for some heavy yardage and get us near field goal range.

▲ *To throw a "Hail Mary" pass, turn to page 66.*

▲ *To pitch out to your running back, turn to page 68.*

With 45 seconds to play, the Panthers are in a nickel formation: They have four down linemen at the line of scrimmage, just two linebackers behind them, and five defensive backs instead of the usual four. This is a pass-prevent defense. Obviously the Panthers smell a *big* pass play coming up.

It's first-and-10 from the Rebels 22-yard line, and Carolina trails 34–33. Rabbit lines up in the shotgun, about six yards behind the center. This will give him a better view of the field and a little more time before he has to throw. Jackson is wide left, Kirby is wide right, and Finch is in close to the right, which becomes the Rebs' strong side. The rest of the team is in a standard pro set.

There's the snap. Rabbit drops back even farther. It looks like he's going to go deep with a "Hail Mary." Rabbit releases the ball . . . it's flying and . . . *intercepted!*

All the Panthers have to do now is run out the clock. And that's exactly what they do. The Carolina Rebels lose, 34–33, and the Philadelphia Panthers are on their way to their third Super Bowl.

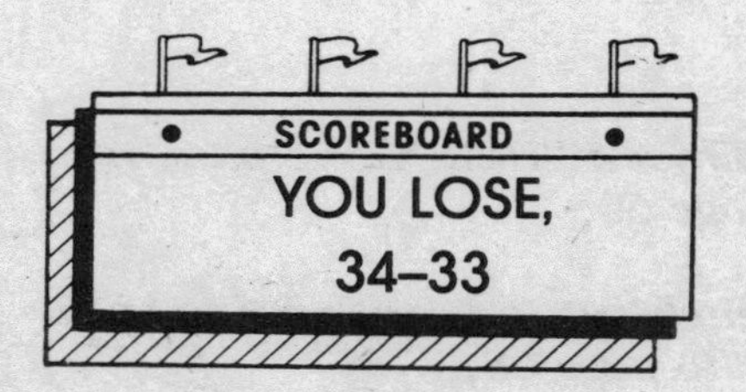

7

There are 45 seconds to play, and the Panthers have gone to their nickel defense: four down linemen, only two linebackers and five defensive backs. This pass-prevent formation is a clear indication that the Panthers expect the Rebel offense to go to the air.

The Rebs come up to the 22-yard line in a standard pro set, with running backs Wicker and Dogan and fullback Tiger Smith behind Rabbit. Tight end Killer Kirby lines up left, along with wide receiver Boris Finch. Split end Moe Jackson is wide to the right. I expected to see them send more receivers, Duke.

Rabbit calls out signals. The center snaps the ball. Rabbit pitches out to Wicker, who sweeps left, gaining some extra blocking from Kirby and Smith. Wicker is brought down by one of the Panther safeties after a pickup of 19 yards. Great run. It's a first down on the Rebels 41.

Good play, but not enough. With only half a minute on the clock, I've really got to call the right play now if we're going to pull this baby out. My first thought is to throw the ball toward the sidelines, where it's less likely to be intercepted. If the pass is incomplete it'll stop the clock, and if it's complete we have the first down and time for one more play to set up the

field goal. But if it *is* intercepted . . . well, that's not worth thinking about now. A better option might be to pass deep and go for the touchdown now.

▲ *To pass deep, turn to page 70.*

▲ *To throw toward the sidelines, turn to page 72.*

It's first-and-10 now, with just 28 seconds on the clock. The Rebel offense is on its 41-yard line in a standard pro set. Nells Wicker and Clancy Dogan are behind Rabbit. Killer Kirby and Moe Jackson line up left, while Boris Finch is wide to the right. The defense goes into a 4-3-4 alignment, ready for either a run or a pass.

"Rabbit looks up and down, then barks out the signals. After the snap, he drops back, looking for a receiver. But no . . . the blitz is on!

"The Panthers are all over Rabbit, Duke. He's out flat behind the line of scrimmage. What a loss! Now it's second down with 13 yards to go."

"Apparently Rabbit took a blow to his knee, Jay. He's being assisted off the field. This is a *very* bad break for the Carolina Rebels. Without Rabbit, they have very little chance of scoring in these last few seconds. . . ."

I can't believe I'm stuck on the sidelines. All the Panthers have to do is keep us out of field-goal range for two plays.

That's exactly what they do. Both passes we try are incomplete and we are forced to turn the ball over to the Panthers. All I can do is sit here and watch in frustration as the clock runs out. We lose by one point, 34–33, and instead of going to the Super Bowl, we're heading home.

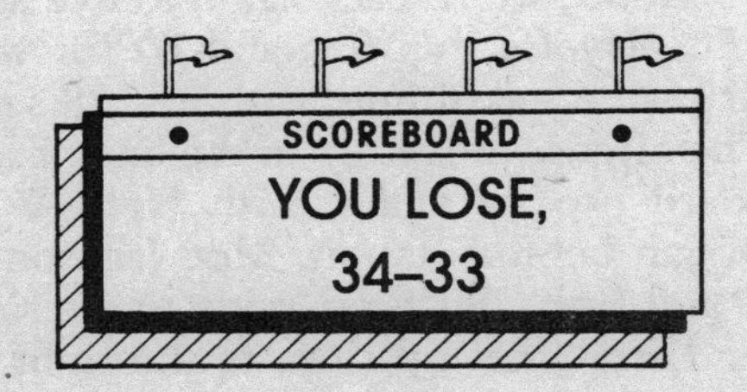

Well folks, we're back again to live action here at the NFL playoffs. It's first-and-10 for the Rebels from their own 41-yard line, with just 28 seconds left to play. The offense moves up to the line of scrimmage in a standard pro set again, with Nells Wicker and Clancy Dogan behind Rabbit, Moe Jackson out wide to the left and Boris Finch out wide to the right. Tight end Killer Kirby lines up close to the right this time.

The Panther defense is set up in a standard 4-3-4 alignment, alert for a possible run.

There's the snap. It looks like Rabbit is handing off to Wicker, who takes off right. But wait . . . it's a fake. Rabbit still has the ball, folks. He's going for the pass, rolling right and searching out a sideline receiver. He found him. He throws to Boris Finch, and the pass is complete.

Finch is finally brought down at the Panther 47. Now, its first down, and more important, the Carolina Rebels are getting close to field-goal range.

The clock is still running. There're only 16 seconds left and the Rebels go without a huddle. It's a play-action fake. Rabbit fakes the handoff to Wicker. While the Panther linebackers go after Wicker, Rabbit gets a quick bullet pass off to Kirby behind the Panther linebackers. It's complete! Kirby has running room, and he's off. He's at the 40 . . . the 35 . . . the 25 and he goes all the way. *Touchdown!* Lou Vanunzo makes the extra point, and the buzzer sounds to end the game. The visiting Carolina Rebels win, 40–34, and Rabbit leads his team to their first-ever berth in the Super Bowl!

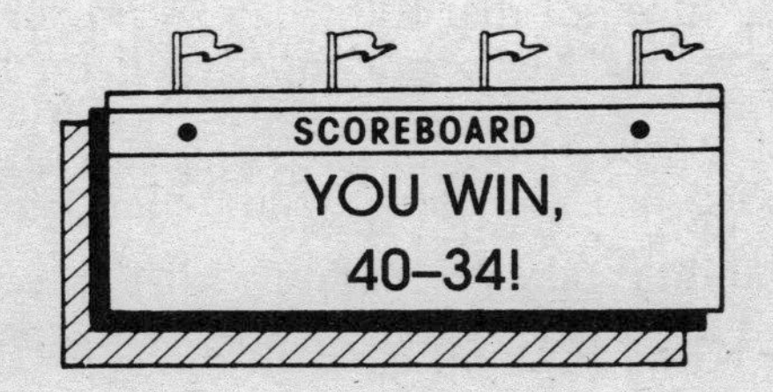

That interception was a really tough break for the Carolina Rebels. Now, with a little more than a minute and a half left to play, the visitors are on their own 36-yard line and trailing by six points, making the score 33–27. The Panthers have their nickel defense in place: They've got four down linemen at the line of scrimmage, only two linebackers and five defensive backs. With just two linebackers, they'll be weaker against a run, but the extra defensive back will provide better coverage of the Rebels receivers. The Panthers are obviously looking to guard against the pass here.

"The Rebels go into a standard pro set. Rabbit lines up in the shotgun. Moe Jackson is wideout to the left and Killer Kirby is wideout to the right, with Boris Finch also out to the left. There's the snap. Rabbit falls back even farther, and he's definitely going to pass. He's going deep, looking for Kirby . . . and it's complete at the Panther 40-yard line! Kirby breaks free from one of the Panther defensive backs, and he's in the clear at the Panther 35-yard line. He's at the 30 . . . the 20 . . . the 10. Touchdown! What a fabulous play!"

"You've sure got that right, Jay. A 64-yard touchdown, and Killer Kirby got most of it on his own. Amazing!"

"Here comes Lou Vanunzo to kick the extra point. The ball is up . . . and it's good!

"The Panthers take possession with 42 seconds left, but they fail to advance. That means the Carolina Reb-

els are on their way to the Super Bowl, winning the American Football Conference championship by the slimmest of margins, 34–33."

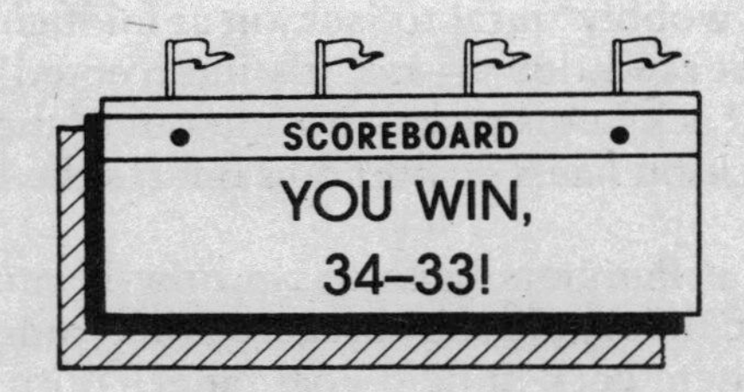

The Rebels trail by six, 33–27, with just a little more than a minute and a half to play. It's first-and-10 for the visitors on their own 36. The Panthers have gone into their nickel defense, with four down linemen, just two linebackers instead of the standard three, and five defensive backs. This weakens them against the run but helps their coverage of the Rebel receivers. The Panthers clearly expect Carolina to pass. The Rebs are in a standard pro formation, with Rabbit directly behind the center, Jackson and tight end Kirby to the left, and Finch to the right.

"After the snap, Rabbit drops back into the pocket. He fires a bullet to Moe Jackson . . . and it's complete at the 41! Jackson is downed at the Rebel 43, for a gain of 7 yards. And so the Rebs face second-and-3. The clock is running. Rabbit calls an audible at the line of scrimmage. He goes to the air again, this time over the top to Boris Finch. The pass is complete for 5 yards and a first down. Well, what do you think, Duke?"

"The strategy seems to be working, Jay—they're going without a huddle and moving quickly into Panther territory. There's the snap . . . another pass. This time it's a wobbly spiral to Jackson at midfield, but it's tipped, knocked down—no, it's intercepted! Panther defensive back Louis picked it right out of the air after the tip. Jackson hauls down Louis but it's the Panthers' ball.

"All the Panthers have to do now is run out the clock. But they suddenly break a long running play that puts them back in field-goal range. With less than

15 seconds to go, their kicker hits a beauty for the field goal that clinches the game. The Panthers win the AFC championship, 36–27."

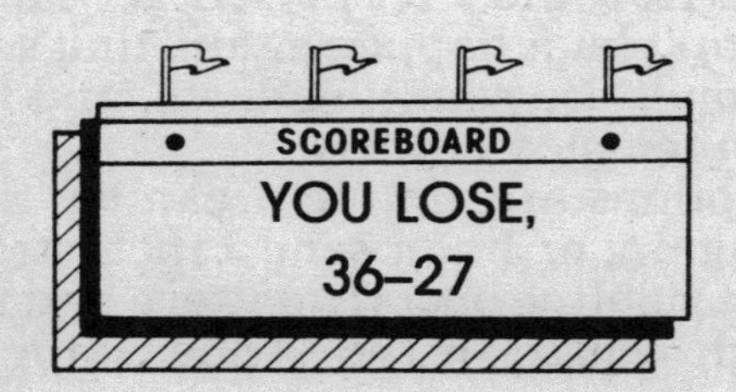

There's one minute and fifty seconds left in regulation time, and the Rebels have a second down with 5 yards to go at the Panther 34-yard line. Rabbit is lining up in the shotgun, with Moe Jackson wide to the left and Killer Kirby wide to the right. Finch goes in motion, left to right. There's the snap. Rabbit steps back even farther, searching for an open receiver. He's looking for a receiver in the end zone. But the blitz is on, and before he can get the ball in the air, Rabbit is slammed by a Panther linebacker and sacked for a loss on the play. It's a tough break for the Rebs."

"That's right, Jay. Rabbit was dropped at the Panther 41, making this a third-and-12 situation."

"Well, Duke, let's see how Rabbit handles the pressure now. He is facing the Rebels' most important play of the game."

Jeez! How did I let myself get sacked like that? I can't let it happen again, that's for sure. The seconds are counting down, and I need to call another play quickly.

My options are simple. I can try the "Hail Mary" again, or I can send Finch straight up the right sideline on a fly pattern and try to hit him with a pass in full stride. With luck he

could go all the way for a touchdown. This assumes, of course, that he can get open and that our timing is perfect.

▲ *To throw another "Hail Mary" pass, turn to page 82.*

▲ *To call the fly pattern, turn to page 83.*

The Rebels need to gain 5 yards for the first down, as they line up on second down at the Panther 34. There's 1:50 on the clock. The Rebs are in a standard pro set, with Wicker and Dogan behind Rabbit, tight end Kirby lined up left, and split end Jackson wide to the right. The Panther defense is in a 4-3-4 alignment. They look ready for either a run or a pass.

Rabbit looks at the defense as the ball is snapped. He hands off to Wicker, who runs left. The Panther linebackers stop him just over the line of scrimmage and Wicker is dropped at the 33. That leaves the Rebs with a third down and 4 yards to go.

I wouldn't have minded getting a little more yardage on that play, but we're still OK. For this next play, I could call a run up the middle to get us closer, or bring in our kicker to try a field goal. A quick field goal, however, might give the Panthers enough time to come back and tie us—or even to score a TD and win.

▲ *To kick the field goal, turn to page 84.*

▲ *To run up the middle, turn to page 86.*

The clock reads 1:29 as the Rebels take their positions at the Panther 41. Rabbit lines up in the shotgun again, with Jackson on the left and and Finch and Kirby out right, making the right the Rebels' strong side. The Panther defense counters with a nickel formation, using five defensive backs and only two linebackers. Obviously they smell another pass play coming up.

"There's the snap. Rabbit wants to pass again. He throws deep toward the end zone. But it's intercepted just short of the goal line! The defender runs the ball all the way back to the Panther 22."

"That ball was a bit underthrown, Jay. Another tough break for the Rebs."

"The Panthers aren't wasting any time, either, Duke. A few quick passing plays put them into field-goal range. Only seconds remain as their kicker attempts the field goal . . . and it's good. The Panthers win by 3, taking the AFC championship and a spot in the Super Bowl."

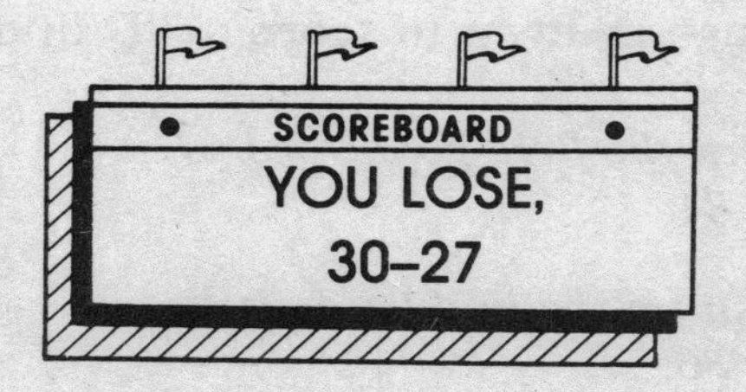

The Rebels face a third-and-12 situation as they line up at the Panther 41-yard line. There's 1:29 left in the fourth quarter of this 27–27 game. Rabbit lines up in the shotgun again. Kirby and Finch are out to the right, Jackson to the left. The Panthers come in with their nickel defense, using just two linebackers and five defensive backs. This pass-prevent formation will provide maximum coverage of the Rebel receivers.

The ball is snapped to Rabbit. He drops back, looking for a receiver. This time he looks to the right where Finch has cut to the sideline. Rabbit releases the ball . . . and Finch makes a beautiful over-the-shoulder catch. There's nothing but open field ahead of him. He's at the 15 . . . the 10 . . . he scores! A great play, Duke, and an excellent call. The extra point puts the Rebels ahead by 7.

The Panthers receive the ball on the kickoff, but with less than a minute left, they barely advance to their own 40 before the buzzer sounds. The Carolina Rebels win the AFC championship, 34–27, and two weeks from now they will battle the NFC champions in the Super Bowl!

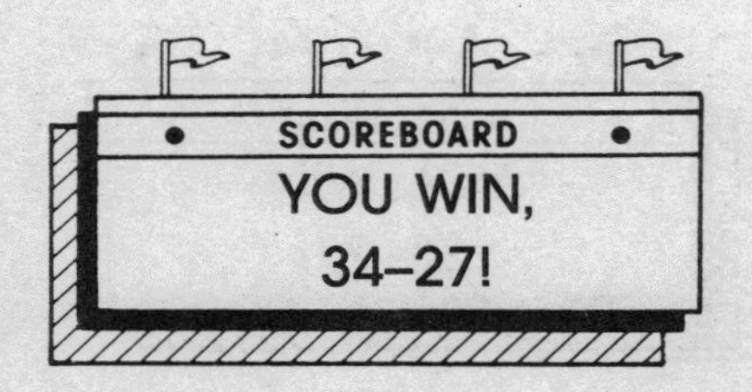

There's 1:27 left to play, and the Rebels have a third down and 4 yards to go at the Panther 33. The Rebs kicking unit is taking the field. It looks like they're not going to take any foolish chances, Duke. They want a quick three points now. The ball is snapped, and Lou Vanunzo gets a boot into it . . . the ball is high and straight and splits the uprights. Carolina has pulled ahead by three!"

"With just over a minute left to play, it will take some fast action for the Panthers to recover from this blow, Jay."

They're taking over the ball at their 35 on the kick. The Panther quarterback completes a few short passes, but they're not enough. The clock winds down and the Carolina Rebels win the AFC championship, 30–27!

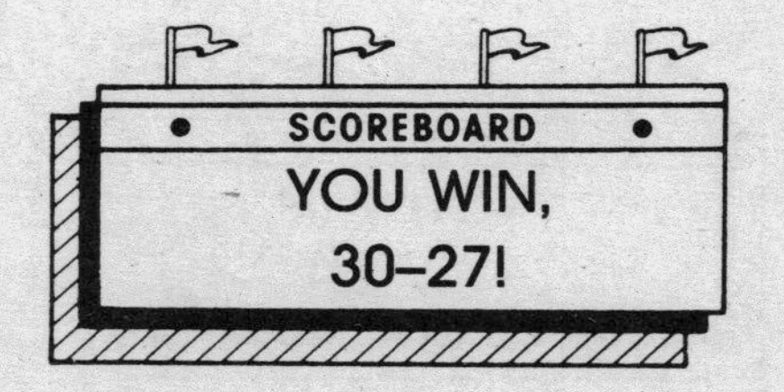

The clock shows 1:27 remaining as the Rebels break their huddle. They face a third-and-4 situation at the Panther 33. The running backs Wicker and Smith are behind Rabbit, Kirby and Jackson are out to the left, while Finch is out to the right. The defense goes into a run-prevent formation, with three down linemen, four linebackers, and four defensive backs who play close to the line.

"There's the snap, and Rabbit hands off to Wicker, who follows Smith's blocking up the middle. But the hole closes quickly and Wicker is stopped at the 31. That makes it fourth-and-2. I'm sure they'll go for the field goal, Duke."

"Right you are, Jay. Here comes Lou Vanunzo."

"The ball is snapped and Vanunzo kicks the ball squarely . . . but it's blocked! The Panthers pounce on the loose ball and take possession at their own 35. Time runs out and this tie game is going into overtime.

"The Panthers win the coin toss and they have plenty of time now. Philadelphia moves into field-goal range—and the kick is good. The Rebels never get a chance as the Panthers claim the sudden-death victory, 30–27, and win the AFC championship."

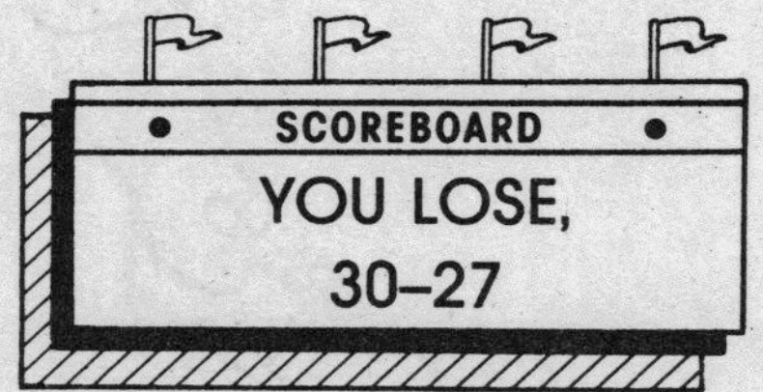

The Rebels kicking team takes the field at the Panther 7-yard line with 58 seconds left to play. There's the snap, the ball is placed, and a terrific Panther rush is on. But Lou Vanunzo, the Rebel kicker, gets the ball up; and the kick is good! With 54 seconds left on the clock, the Rebels take a 3-point lead."

"It looks like three points will prove to be enough, Jay. The Panthers receive the kickoff, but there just isn't enough time left for them to strike back. A 52-yard last-second field-goal attempt flies wide of the goalposts. The Carolina Rebels win the AFC championship, 30–27, and are heading to their first appearance in the Super Bowl!"

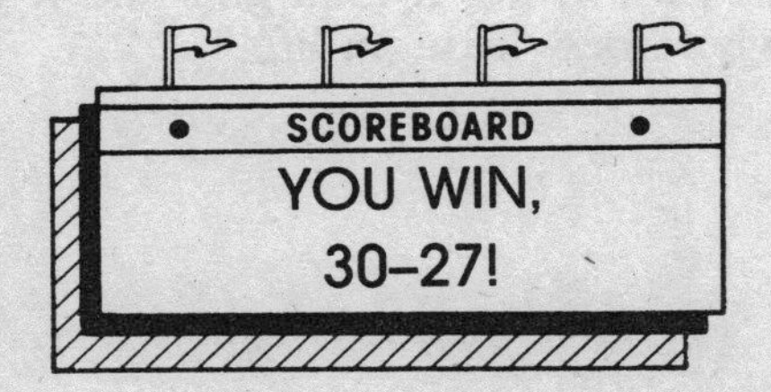

It's fourth-and-1 and there are just 58 seconds left on the clock as the Rebels move back to the line of scrimmage at the Panther 7-yard line. This is amazing, Duke. The Rebels are going to try to get the first down rather than kick the field goal and take the lead in this game."

"I think this is a huge mistake, Jay."

"The Rebels line up in a standard pro formation. Running backs Wicker and Dogan are behind Rabbit. Jackson goes out wide left and Finch is wide right, while Killer Kirby is in close to the left, giving the Rebels extra power on that side. The Panthers have gone back to their 4-3-4 defense, ready for either a run or a pass.

"The center snaps the ball, and Rabbit hands off to Wicker. Wicker drives ahead, searching for a hole, but he has no open ground to work with. He is brought down at what looks like the original line of scrimmage. Oh, my! This is close. The officials are coming out to measure, Duke."

"Wicker got it, Jay. Yes, the referee signals first down at the Panther 6! What an incredible play. I still don't agree with it, but it took guts and it gives the Rebels a whole new lease on life."

What a big play! The clock's ticking down. A running play is in order; we don't want to run the risk of an interception when we're so close. The worst that can happen if they hold us is that we get another chance to kick the field goal. Maybe I'll hand off to Dogan for a run up the right side. On the other hand, I could try to sneak the ball up the middle myself. They wouldn't be expecting it and since I wouldn't have to hand the ball off, the defense would be less likely to sack me behind the line of scrimmage.

▲ *To run the ball up the side, turn to page 90.*

▲ *To try a quarterback sneak, turn to page 91.*

It's first-and-goal as the Rebels return to the line of scrimmage at the Panther 6-yard line. With 41 seconds remaining. The Rebels go into their one-back offense, with only Dogan behind Rabbit and with two tight ends on the field. This will help the running back get good blocking on either side of the field. The Panther defense is set up in a 3-4-4 run-prevent formation.

There's the snap. Rabbit gives the ball to Dogan, who sprints right. But he's nailed behind the line of scrimmage for a loss of three yards. The clock is running, with about 30 seconds left.

Rabbit doesn't hesitate, however. The Rebs are back at the line of scrimmage. Rabbit calls the signals. There's the snap . . . and Rabbit goes down in one of the quickest sacks in history! The Panthers continue this stringent stand. At fourth down, the Rebels try for the field goal with 14 seconds remaining. But it's no good, and we're heading into overtime.

Then, one and a half minutes into sudden-death overtime, the Panther quarterback throws a 67-yard pass for a touchdown to win the game, 33–27. What a comeback! The Rebels came so close, but it is the Panthers who will be going to the Super Bowl!

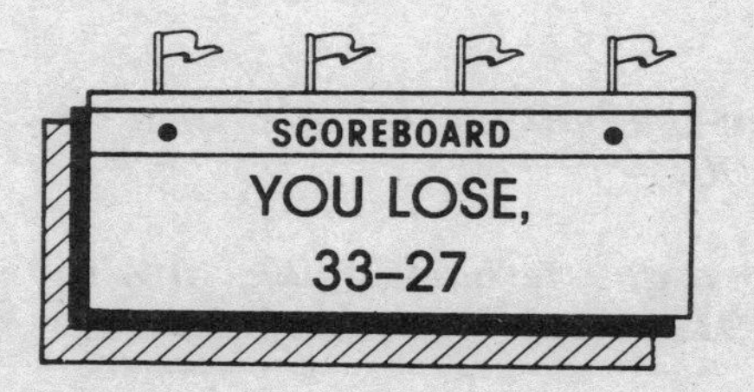

With just 41 seconds to play, the Rebel offense returns to the line of scrimmage. It's first-and-goal from the Panther 6-yard line. The visitors line up in a one-back formation with running back Clancy Dogan behind Rabbit and two tight ends now in the game. The Panthers set up in their 3-4-4 run-prevent defense.

Rabbit barks out the signals on a quick count. The ball is snapped, and Rabbit hands off to Dogan. But no—he faked the handoff. It's a quarterback sneak! Rabbit runs up the middle behind center Breaker Brown . . . he breaks into the open and Rabbit has it! Touchdown! The extra point is good, and the Rebels pull ahead by 7 with just 26 seconds left in the game.

The Panthers receive the kickoff, but they don't have time to recover. Even a field goal wouldn't help them here. The Carolina Rebels come out on top, 34–27, taking the AFC championship for the first time ever and moving on to face the NFC champs in the Super Bowl.

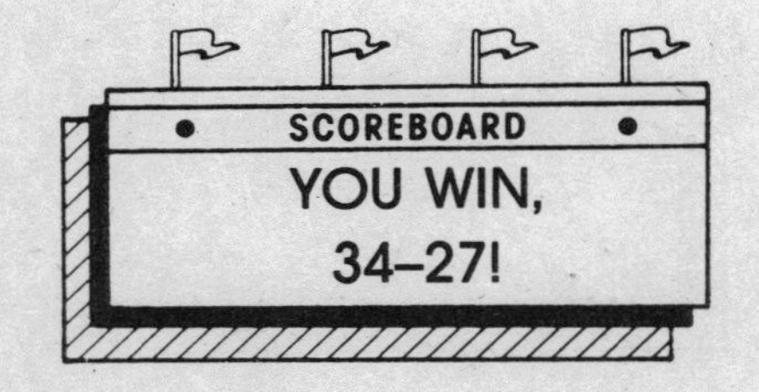